# The Car Trip

**Matt Sims**

**High Noon Books**
Novato, California

**Editor: Susan Blackaby**
**Cover and Interior Illustrations: Rick Hackney**



International Standard Book Number: 1-57128-196-7

9 8 7 6 5 4 3 2
0 9 8 7 6 5 4 3

# Contents

The Plan........................1
The Trip........................5
On the Road..................9
The Plains...................13
Up in the Hills ...........18
The West Coast..........22

# The Plan

Dad had a plan to drive from coast to coast.

"This is the way we can go," said Dad.

He had a map to show Roy the roads. "Here we are in the East. We live in New

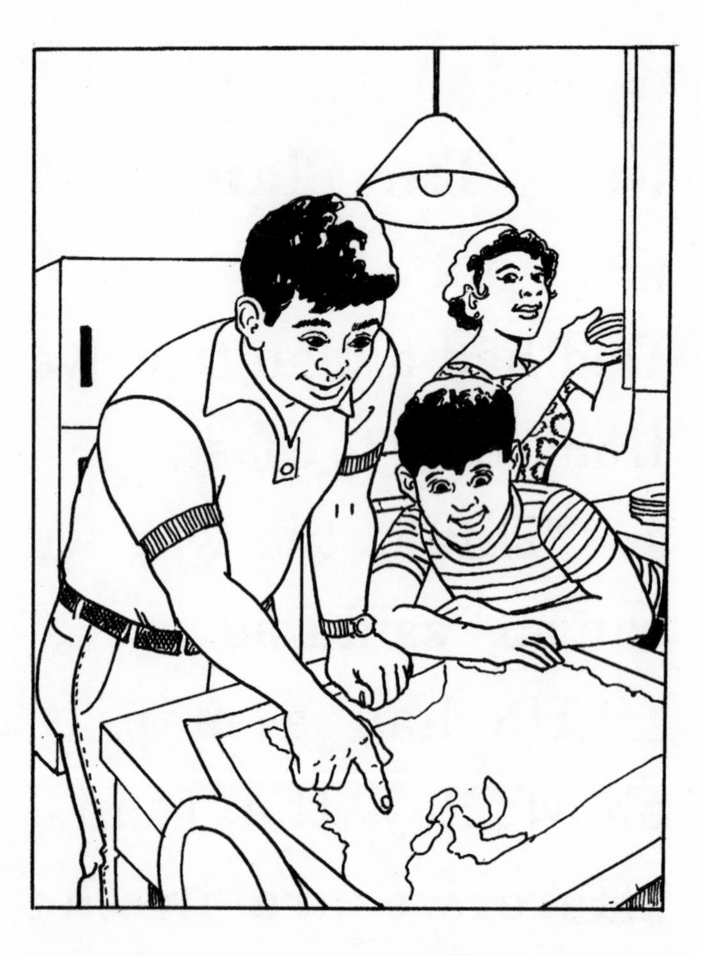

*Dad had a plan to drive from coast to coast.*

York. We will drive west. We will see lots of states. We can camp and fish as we go if it does not rain."

"What will we do when we get to the end?" said Roy.

"We will come back," said Dad.

"That will be fun," said Roy. "Will Mom come, too?"

"No," said Dad. "Mom will stay home. She wants to take a class while we take our trip."

Dad made a list of what to pack. Roy put his stuff in a bag. He gave the bag a zip.

"That was quick," said Dad.

"Well, I can not wait," said Roy.

## The Trip

At last, the day came for Dad and Roy to go. Mom gave them a hug and a kiss.

"You take care," said Mom. "Send me lots of cards."

"We will," said Roy

*"Send me lots of cards," said Mom.*

and Dad.

And off they went.

It took a while to get out of New York. It is a big state! But then they came to the state line.

"Now I feel like we are on our way," said Dad.

"Me, too," said Roy. "And in a few days we will be at the beach!"

*Hi Mom,*

*It is our first day out of the state. We took a dip in a lake. The lake was huge. It was like the sea. Do you miss us yet?*

*Roy*

# On the Road

The road went on and on. There was so much to see.

"This is a big land," said Roy.

"You said it," said Dad.

Dad and Roy had a

good time. Dad had a lot of car games to play.

"We can sing songs like my dad and I did on trips," said Dad.

"Grand Dad can sing?" said Roy.

"You bet," said Dad. "He has a good voice. He knows a lot of songs, too."

*Dad had a lot of car games to play.*

*Hi Mom,*

*It is hard to think of what it was like to walk on the trail west. The land goes on for miles. All you can see is dust and sky. I am glad I am in a car with Dad and not on foot with a big ox.*

*Roy*

# The Plains

Dad and Roy had to cross the plains. It was hot. The land was the same for miles and miles.

"This will be a long drive," said Dad. "Try to tune in the ball game. We can hear the Mets play the Cubs."

Roy found the game. It came in loud and clear. It was the top of the first.

"Just in time," said Dad.

Just then, the car went bump, bump, bump. Dad had to pull off the road at a wide spot.

"We have a flat tire,"

Dad said.

They got the good tire out of the trunk.

"Hand me the jack," said Dad.

Roy held the lug nuts while Dad did the work. Roy saw a nail in the flat tire.

"We can get a patch at the next stop," said Dad.

*They got the good tire out of the trunk.*

*Hi Mom,*

*We had a flat! Dad was mad. It made him miss the big play of the game. We ate a big meal while a man put a patch on the tire. Then we went on our way. We will be out of the plains soon!*

*Roy*

# Up in the Hills

The hills rose out of the plains. They were so tall. They had snow on their tops. Roy saw a moose by a creek. He saw a goat on a cliff. He saw deer in the woods.

Dad and Roy went to

*Roy saw a moose by a creek.*

a place to camp. They set up the tent. Then they went to the creek and got three fish to eat. Hoot owls flew from tree to tree.

"I can hear things howl and growl," said Roy.

"Tell them to pipe down," said Dad. "We need to sleep."

*Hi Mom,*

*We left the plains and are now in the hills. Dad and I like to camp. It is fun to sleep in the tent. Dad wants to stay in a lodge next. He said I need a bath. But I want to wait till we reach the coast. Then I can take a bath in the sea!*

*Roy*

# The West Coast

Roy and Dad drove down from the South Pass.

They saw a lot of ranch land as they drove west.

At last, Dad and Roy got to the beach on the

*At last, Dad and Roy got to the beach on the West Coast.*

West Coast. They sat on the sand. The sea was at their feet. They were on the rim of the land.

"We made it," said Dad.

"Yes, we did," said Roy. "It has been such a fun trip. But I will be glad to get home to see Mom and tell her all of our tales."

*Hi Mom,*

*Here we are on the West Coast. We spent the day at the beach. It is nice to sit in the sun and look out to sea. We ate crab. We will camp at the state park. Then we will go east and make our way back home. See you soon.*

*Roy*

## High Frequency Words

| | | |
|---|---|---|
| been | have | there |
| come | of | they |
| do | put | to |
| does | said | were |
| from | the | what |
| goes | their | |